P9-CBY-970

Desert
-
Sea

Desert - Sea

Fauna
of the Saudi-Arabian
Red Sea coast

Hagen Schmid

RED FIREFISH   *Pterois volitans*   Linnaeus 1758

Hagen Schmid

CONTENTS

Jürgen Kuchinke

Contributing photographers in alphabetical order:

Peter Dixon

Bizzie Frost

John & Patsy Gasperetti

Simon Hackett

Jürgen Kuchinke

Walter Lüdin

Kevin Metcalfe

Tuula Metcalfe

Simon Priscott

Gerry Pyke

Hagen Schmid

Hans Sjöholm

Charles Zoch

CAMERA GEAR USED:

UW Cameras:	Nikonos III, IV, V
	with 35, 28 and 15 mm UW-Nikkor lenses
	Nikonos Close-Up and Macro extension tubes with 35 mm lens
Camera housings:	Tussey Pro Line, Subal Miniflex, Aquatica, Hugyfot
Cameras:	Nikon F3, Nikon 8001, Canon F1
Lenses:	Macro-Nikkor 105 and 60 mm, Canon 105 Macro
UW Flashes:	Ikelite 225, Ikelite 150, Ikelite MS, Sub sea 150, Nikonos SB 103, Sunpak marine 2400
Film material:	Fuji 100, Fuji Velvia, Kodak 64X, Kodak 100 Professional

ACKNOWLEDGEMENTS

I like to thank all of the people and close friends who helped and assisted me to produce this book.

Special thanks to the scientists Dr. Nathalie Yonow for identifying the nudibranchs and Dr. Michael Türkay for classifying the crustaceans.

I am also grateful to Aramco World for permitting me to use their excellent map of the Arabian Peninsula.

As well I want to mention Dagmar Kuchinke for spotting so many hidden creatures for the photographers.

And I thank my lovely wife Nylka who spent many long hours translating and typing all the texts and for tolerating my long absences while travelling to the Red Sea to collect all the needed material and information.

FOREWORD

In October 1975 I flew across the Red Sea from Port Sudan to Jeddah, my first visit to Saudi Arabia. From the air, before the plane landed, I saw a beautiful fringing reef along the shore to the south of the city. I was unable to find any dive gear in Jeddah at that time to explore the reef, so I decided to snorkel. Finally I ended up on the reef to the north which was clear and pristine.

On my second visit to Saudi Arabia in 1978 I met Hagen Schmid who then had logged over 1000 hours of diving in the Red Sea off Jeddah and its environs. He took me diving at some very interesting sites, and we have been in contact ever since.

Hagen came to Jeddah in 1971 when it began to grow from a town to what today is a metropolis of nearly two million inhabitants. An inevitable consequence of Jeddah's rapid growth has been the impact upon its coastal marine life. Unfortunately many of the reefs near the city, that were in such good condition twenty years ago, are no longer so healthy. Pollution, siltation and other human factors have taken their toll.

In 1974 Hagen, together with Saudi businessman Abdul Hameed Bokhari, opened the first dive shop in Saudi Arabia. He wanted to encourage more people to SCUBA dive and snorkel in local waters and to gain an appreciation of the unique and magnificent biota of the Red Sea. With this appreciation he hoped there would be an awareness of the need to protect the reefs and its colourful corals, fishes, and other marine animals.

In 1979 Hagen and Dr. Peter Vine co-operated in the production of "Colourful Saudi Arabian Red Sea", the first book on the Red Sea marine life of the nation, featuring underwater photographs. The 2500 copies are collectors' items today. A follow-up, "Saudi Arabian Red Sea", has appeared in five editions (over 20,000 copies) and is still one of the most informative books on Red Sea reefs.

In recent years Hagen has been collecting the best photographs from the most devoted and gifted nature photographers in Saudi Arabia. He has brought these together in this outstanding book under the title **Desert Sea**. Most photographs appear with a short but informative text. Like his previous books, it will surely enlighten and fascinate the reader. It should help promote the need to establish marine preserves along the coast of Saudi Arabia to prevent further depredations by man.

Dr. John E. Randall
Marine Biologist
Bernice P. Bishop Museum
Honolulu/Hawaii

INTRODUCTION

In the past the bird and mammal populations of the Arabian Peninsula were well protected by the physical size of the country and its sparsely inhabited deserts. With the discovery of large oil deposits, and following the introduction of industrialisation in the Middle East, extensive road construction commenced, opening up the region.

The Bedouins could now transport their herds to previously inaccessible sites, where the meagre growth of vegetation was grazed by goats and sheep, reducing food supply for wild gazelles and other native herbivores. Four-wheel drive vehicles allowed hunting parties, armed with powerful fire arms, to drive deep into once remote areas. Overhunting and disappearance of natural habitat brought many species to the threshold of extinction.

A few years ago several Arabian countries started extensive programmes to breed and to re-introduce endangered species into the wild. Protected areas have been established to enable animals, like the Arabian gazelle, the oryx and the tahr, to roam freely again across the wide deserts and high mountains of these magnificent countries.

The story of the Arabian oryx is a particularly good and unique example of how Man can help to rescue wildlife. From a stock of only a few wild caught animals a sizable herd of captive bred oryx was created, which led to their release back to the Arabian deserts. Today large herds of these ungulates are once more living in the wild.

Sadly, other species, like the Arabian ostrich and the onager, a wild donkey, became extinct before recent conservation efforts took hold.

In the early seventies I had the opportunity to explore the Red Sea coral reefs and their marine life in the central part of this most northern coral sea. Its richness was a far cry from what we find today.

Steep drop offs close to the city of Jeddah and Yanbu were covered with black coral trees, resembling underwater forests. Large fan corals swayed in the currents, giving shelter to colourful small fish and invertebrates. Large schools of mackerel and other schooling fish were attracted by the rising air bubbles from the diver's breathing apparatus and they surrounded the intruder like a living silver wall.

Today these former coral gardens are bare walls; the sea has been plundered by greed and carelessness. The black coral trees are used as decoration and dust collectors in living rooms. Sea fans are squeezed between glass plates, decorated with plastic sea stars and sold as souvenirs.

Sharks are caught by the hundred, their fins are severed and the animals, now unable to swim, are thrown back into the sea and left to die. This is done only to supply Far-Eastern markets with sharkfin soup.

Coral reefs are being dredged to build harbours and marinas. Shallow lagoons are filled in to gain extra land, destroying valuable breeding grounds for many fish.

Boat crews drop their anchors between fragile corals, ruining in seconds what took many years to grow.

Sewage water from the cities is pumped into the sea and encourages algae to grow. The algae in turn is smothering and killing extensive coral reefs.

The photographs in this book may give the impression of a still perfect under-water world, that today is hardly found anymore. Nowadays when one is diving or snorkelling in these waters, one wonders if this is really the same sea.

Most photographs were taken on days with exceptionally good underwater visibility. Often it took months or years to get a nearly perfect picture. The creatures are shown in their natural environment, which can be between broken corals or on top of sunken shipwrecks.

Whenever known, their common and scientific names, as well as the name and date of the scientist who described them, are given. The texts are kept intentionally short so they do not distract from the different backgrounds, which are used in each photograph. The backgrounds are impressions, collected from the shores of the Red Sea. They show the structure of the ever shifting sand dunes, the date palm trees, the laced wooden window facades and the soft coral sea fans.

We hope that this book helps to encourage the preservation of our seas and wildlife world-wide. Everyone can contribute by not buying sea shells, turtle products or dead corals in souvenir shops, or by not ordering sharkfin soup in a restaurant. Diving and sport shops can stop the sale of underwater spearguns to discourage people from hunting and decimating the fish populations even more. We can all contribute to the effort to preserve our natural resources both on land and in the sea.

Hagen Schmid

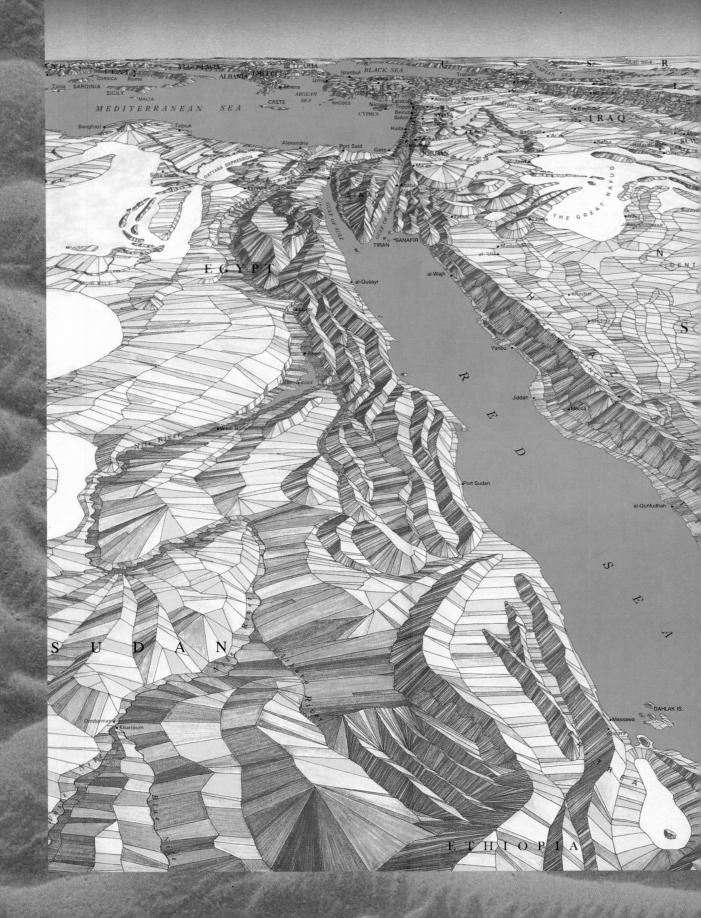

8

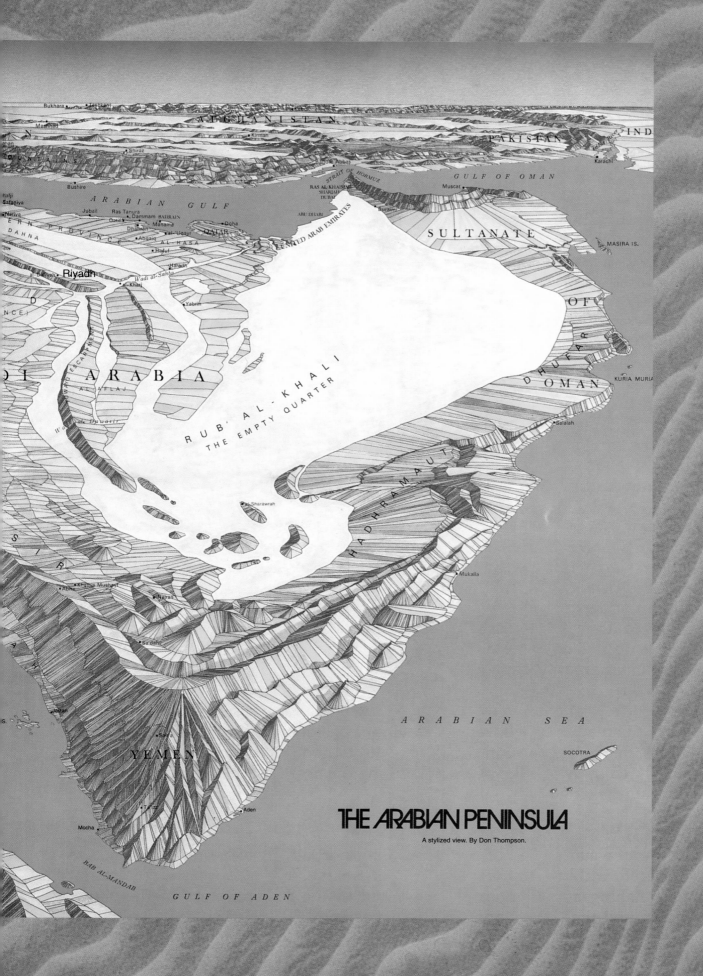

THE ARABIAN PENINSULA

A stylized view. By Don Thompson.

DESERT SEA

Two hundred million years ago the continents of our planet were joined together forming one gigantic landmass called Pangaea. The crustal surface upon which the land rested gradually split into a number of sub-sections (known as tectonic plates). Over the course of millions of years these broke apart from each other and drifted into the positions they occupy today. During this process mountain ranges emerged, oceans disappeared and new ones were formed.

About 70 million years ago the Arabian Peninsula broke away from the African plate and drifted eastwards. A gorge of over 2000 metres deep and 2300 km long was eventually created. Around five million years ago it opened to the south and waters from the Gulf of Aden and the Indian Ocean flooded into the rift that was separating Africa from Arabia, thus beginning the process of forming the 440,000 km² sea known to us as the Red Sea. The process of change continues with the rift widening by as much as several centimetres every year. Wedged between the barren hot shores of two continents, where in summer months air temperatures reach over 40°C and with no major fresh water rivers feeding into it, the Red Sea became the most northern coral sea on our planet. Even at depths of 300–400 metres the water temperature remains constant 21°–22°C, compared to other oceans, where at this depth the temperature is below 10°C.

A somewhat restricted connection (29 km wide and 130 m deep) with the Indian Ocean, at the Straits of Bab el Mandab, combined with the absence of fresh water inflows, creates conditions of higher than average seawater salt-content (salinity). The ancient Red Sea's marine life adapted to these conditions, forming a colourful and appealing underwater realm, where we can find a great diversity of life in sharp contrast to its more desolate shores. Some of the reef dwellers of this nascent ocean occur nowhere else, and many of these endemic species are found only in particular areas of the Red Sea.

Marine life in the southern part of the Red Sea is greatly influenced by the closeness of the plankton rich waters of the Gulf of Aden and is, therefore, different from that of the central portion which, due to its nodal location, experiences very little vertical tidal movement. Species inhabiting the northern section must deal with other conditions including a quite marked drop in water temperatures during the colder winter months.

Open water marine life of the central and northern Red Sea is, in contrast to that associated with the coral reefs, rather sparse. For this reason the major commercial fishing activities are concentrated in the richer waters of the south, especially around the Dahlak and the Farasan Islands.

Low nutrient levels, sparse plankton and the absence of much silt or flotsam, combined with clement weather conditions contribute to good underwater visibility, a factor always appreciated by sport divers.

Sunlight penetrates in much greater depths than is usual under the sea, enabling hardcorals to grow and feed. At depths of well over 30 metres one can find enough light to see long distances and admire the corals which grow there. Corals are comprised tiny individual polyps, whose ability to extract calcium and carbon dioxide from the sea provides the key to their ability to build colonies of the most beautiful and amazing forms. From such small beginnings, great structures are created and large coral reefs can stretch thousands of miles, supporting incredibly rich marine ecosystems that would not exist were it not for the life of the lowly coral polyp.

The contrast between the rich underwater life of the Red Sea and the barren shore appears to be great but, in fact, the coastal littoral and inland areas support a wide variety of wildlife. In this book are photographs, not only of the under sea life but, also, of a few of the striking and diverse creatures found in Saudi Arabia.

Jeddah, the "Bride of the Red Sea", is the main sea port for western Saudi Arabia. It is an ancient and beautiful city – historically the port of entry for the millions of pilgrims who come to Makkah and Madina for the annual Hajj (Pilgrimage). We have, therefore, included a few photographs of this most picturesque of cities, which has stood for many centuries on the edge of the land and the sea and has been nurtured by both.

We hope that we have managed to portray some of the fascinating aspects of the wonderful undersea world by taking a look at the behaviour of some individual species, describing how they adapt to their unique environment and examining how they care for their young; in this way showing that their lives are inextricably woven into the complex web of life that forms one of nature's greatest creations – the coral reefs of the Red Sea.

UNDERWATER PHOTOGRAPHY

In bright sunlight or in near-darkness, at close proximity or at great distance, the human eye is able to see things clearly and sharply. The eye functions so perfectly, that no camera optic can compete with it.

To produce a sharp photographic image, a camera lens must be adjusted or "focused on" the actual object. The area in front or behind will then still be "out of focus" and we get a blurry picture of it. How much will be "in focus", or sharp, depends on the type of optical lens which is used, the opening of the camera's light shutter (controlled, as in the human eye, by the pupil) and the distance to the object. Given the same shutter-speed, or time period of lens-opening, on a bright sunny day the camera's "iris" must be opened only a small amount, allowing sufficient light rays to fall on the film surface to produce a picture. On a cloudy day the camera must have a wider opening, allowing the same amount of light to reach the film. With a small lens opening a larger part of a photograph will be in focus. When photographing in close-up the "depth of field" (part of a picture with a sharp image) becomes very narrow, and reduces even further as one moves closer to one's subject.

The difficulties of underwater photography are compounded by low light intensity (requiring wide lens openings) and the fact that one generally needs to be close to one's subject, making it quite a challenge to produce sharp images. Fortunately technological advances have come to our aid in this quest for the perfect underwater picture. Electronic flash can supply the much needed light but, depending on an animal's colouration and on sediments floating in the water, the artificial light can bounce back towards the camera and thus produce overexposed, pale looking pictures. Alternatively this artificial light source may illuminate unwanted flotsam or debris drifting in the water. In order to keep this potential disturbance to a minimum, a diver must move very carefully in the water taking great care not to stir up silt on the seabed. The underwater photographer must also learn to approach marine creatures without frightening them, always striving to reduce the amount of water between the picture subject and the camera. As we have already indicated, this does not favour a wide depth of field.

Taking into consideration that some of the creatures underwater are extremely shy and fast moving and that the diver, at best a cumbersome intruder to this marine-world, is being buffeted by waves and currents (especially at shallow depths), one may gain a small glimpse of the problems facing the underwater photographer.

A successful diver-photographer must understand how marine creatures behave and should build a special rapport with his chosen subjects. At the same time he must bear in mind the entire surroundings, composing both back and foregrounds and positioning himself correctly with respect to photographic requirements. For example, a fish should always swim into a picture and never out of it; and the head, and especially the eye, must be absolutely in focus. Such photographic skills require considerable experience.

The tools of underwater photographers are either land cameras mounted in a waterproof housing or waterproof cameras. The advantage of a camera system in a housing is the flexibility to use different optical lenses which can be fitted and allow the operator to "zoom in" on an object. The waterproof cameras have the advantage of being smaller and they can be more easily handled and transported above and under water.

One way to begin to learn this art is to study other people's results. We hope, in this book, to inspire photographers and to help all its readers to achieve a deeper understanding and respect for our beautiful, but fragile, marine world.

Anemonefish are small colourful creatures of the damselfish family and a favourite subject for the underwater photographer. The genus *Amphiprion* to which these fish belong, consists of 25 species. They always live symbiotically, in association with sea anemones which are themselves invertebrates that feed on fish and other creatures. The anemone's tentacles are armed with countless poisonous stinging cells and are coated with mucus. When these stinging-cells come into contact with a potential victim, they eject stinging threads like harpoons, and thus paralyse the prey.

Anemonefish can swim into these tentacles without being stung. They cover themselves with the mucus of the anemone in which they intend to live and are not then recognized as prey.

It is known that at least one anemonefish, *Amphiprion clarki*, which lives in the *Stichodactyla haddoni* anemone, produces a thick mucus cover, which is similar to the anemone's and is accepted by the *Stichodactyla*.

The largest fish in a pair or group is always female, having changed sex and developed from the most dominant male within a small family group. Such family groups comprise a leading member of each sex and the other members remain juvenile until a leading animal dies. When this happens, one of the juveniles will rapidly become adult to take the place of the lost one.

The female *Amphiprion* deposits between 500 and 1500 eggs on a rock under her anemone, where they are fertilized and guarded by the male. After about one week the eggs develop into larvae, which hatch, generally soon after sunset, and are then carried away by the water currents. To protect the eggs and larvae from the anemone's stinging cells the adult fishes, from time to time, take a tentacle into their mouths and rub its mucus over their offspring. The larvae are now not recognized as prey by the anemone and are safe from the stinging cells.

RED SEA ANEMONEFISH   *Amphiprion bicinctus*   Rüppell 1828
SEA ANEMONE   *Stichodactyla mertensii*

Hans Sjöholm

RED SEA ANEMONEFISH guarding eggs

Simon Hackett

RED SEA ANEMONEFISH larvae shortly before hatching

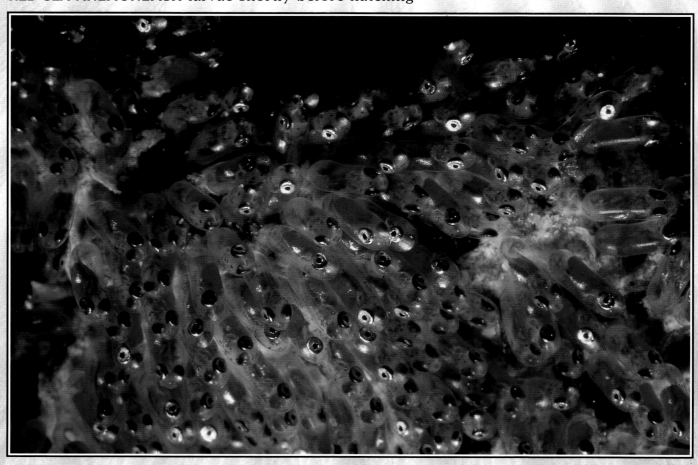

Simon Hackett

RED SEA ANEMONEFISH immunizing nearly-hatched young with sea anemone mucus

Simon Hackett

Juvenile RED SEA ANEMONEFISH

Tuula Metcalfe

THREE-SPOT DASCYLLUS   *Dascyllus trimaculatus*   Rüppell 1828

Tuula Metcalfe

In some instances juvenile three-spot dascyllus use sea anemones as a protective shelter, in the same way that anemonefish do. They adopt similar tactics to those of the anemone-fish to live unharmed in the stinging tentacles.

An abundant group of coral reef fishes is the damselfish *Pomacentridae*. About 320 different species are known to live world-wide, mostly in tropical seas, although some inhabit also cooler temperate waters.

Their feeding and habitat preferences vary greatly. Some feed on algae, others on plankton substances which float in the water currents. The algae feeders tend to protect their territory against any intruder regardless of its size.

Their colouration fluctuates highly from rather drab to very bright colours. Some young fishes display different juvenile colouration.

SULPHUR DAMSELFISH   *Pomacentrus sulfureus*   Klunzinger 1871

Charles Zoch

Kevin Metcalfe

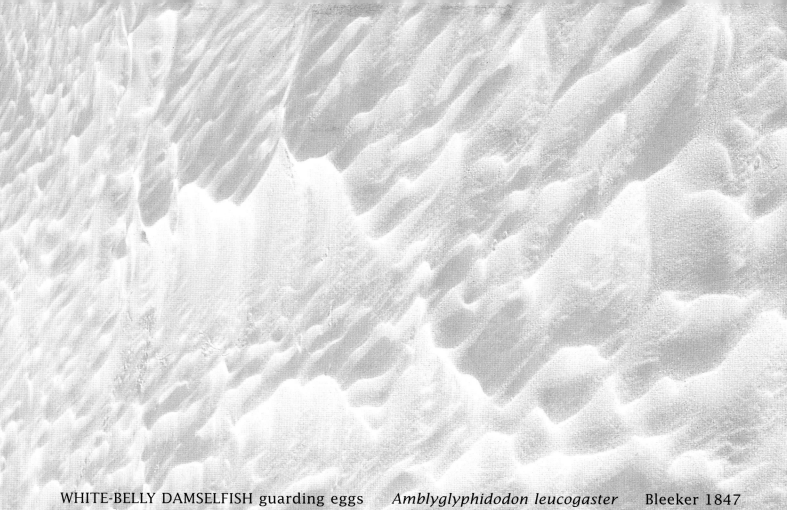

WHITE-BELLY DAMSELFISH guarding eggs   *Amblyglyphidodon leucogaster*   Bleeker 1847

Tuula Metcalfe

Charles Zoch

YELLOWFLANK DAMSELFISH with night-colouration

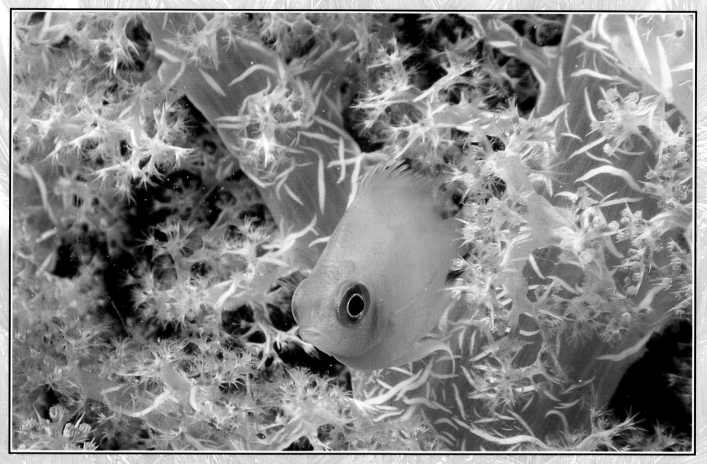

Hans Sjöholm

25

WOLF CARDINALFISH   *Cheilodipterus artus*   Smith 1961

Tuula Metcalfe

During daytime cardinal fishes can be found under shady overhangs and in caves. They are members of the family **APOGONIDAE**, which consists of about 250 species.
The common name is derived from the reddish hue which many display.
Cardinals are nocturnally active; at dusk they leave their daytime retreats in order to feed.
Many cardinals are mouth-brooders. A gelatinous egg-mass is released by the female and is immediately fertilized by the male which later takes the eggs into his mouth for protection.
Males carrying eggs in this manner can easily be distinguished by the enlarged throat region.
Incubation of the eggs lasts several days during which the male brooders do not feed.

THREADFIN CARDINALFISH   *Apogon leptacanthus*   Bleeker 1856

Kevin Metcalfe

FIVELINED CARDINALFISH   *Cheilodipterus quinquelineatus*   Cuvier 1828

Charles Zoch

THREE-SPOT CARDINALFISH   *Apogon trimaculatus*   Cuvier 1828

Charles Zoch

BLACKSTRIPE CARDINALFISH   *Apogon nigrofasciatus*   Lachner 1953

Kevin Metcalfe

Sanganeb island

Hagen Schmid

These strangely shaped fish are known as batfish, or in some areas, spadefish. Scientists classify them in the **EPHIPPIDAE** family.
They can become very curious and closely approach divers.
Their distinctive appearance is enhanced by a silvery colour and circular compressed body.
Young batfish, different, in both colour and shape, from adults, have extremely long fins and resemble drifting leaves.

ORBICULAR BATFISH   *Platax orbicularis*   Forskål 1775

Simon Hackett

Batfish prefer to live in harbour areas with murky water, or around shipwrecks and docks. Schools can contain ten to even several hundred fish, although older individuals tend to live in solitude.
Their diet consists of small invertebrates and zooplankton.

ORBICULAR BATFISH early juvenile stage

Charles Zoch

33

ORBICULAR BATFISH intermediate stage

Hans Sjöholm

Wreck of the *Makkah*

Hans Sjöholm

In 1976 the passenger ship *Makkah* caught fire while moored in Jeddah port. The ship was towed out of the harbour area to her present position, south of Jeddah, where she sank.
The ship's unique, shallow location, close to the city and the reef, makes it a favourite diving site for sport divers. A rich marine fauna has developed on this new artificial reef with soft and hard corals, invertebrates and lots of fish.
During recent years, however, the fish population has suffered a steep decline, because of extensive spearfishing activities.

SOHAL SURGEONFISH   *Acanthurus sohal*   Forskål 1775

Hans Sjöholm

BLUE TANG juvenile *Zebrasoma xanthurum* Blyth 1852

Tuula Metcalfe

These beautiful fish, which feed on plankton and algae, are only found in the coastal waters of the Arabian Peninsula. The blue tang is a rather shy animal, keeping away from divers. By way of contrast, the sohal surgeonfish can become very aggressive, attacking any fish or human diver that enters their reef-top territories. Armed with sharp scalpel-like knives at the base of the tail, they can inflict deep cuts on intruders who refuse to retreat. Scientifically, these fish are members of the **ACANTHURIDAE** family.

SAILFIN TANG early juvenile stage   *Zebrasoma desjardinii*   Bennett 1835

Jürgen Kuchinke

The sailfin tang changes colour and shape in stages while maturing. They are rather shy fish with the young ones frequently hiding among branching corals.

SAILFIN TANG juvenile stage

Jürgen Kuchinke

SAILFIN TANG intermediate stage

Jürgen Kuchinke

SAILFIN TANG adult   *Zebrasoma desjardinii*   Bennett 1835

Jürgen Kuchinke

41

RED FIREFISH early juvenile stage   *Pterois volitans*   Linnaeus 1758

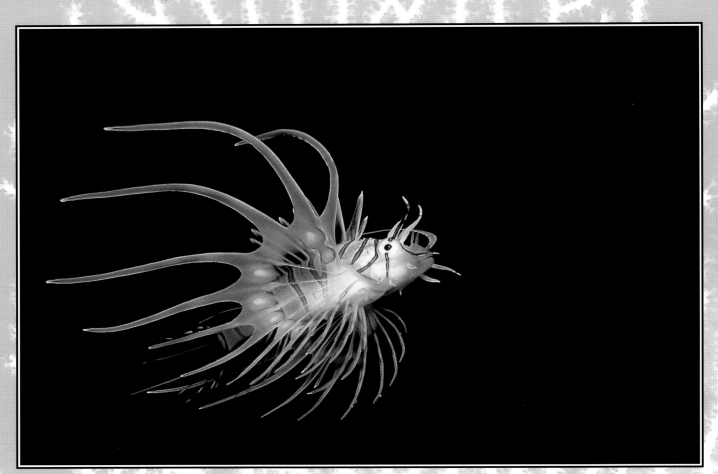

Jürgen Kuchinke

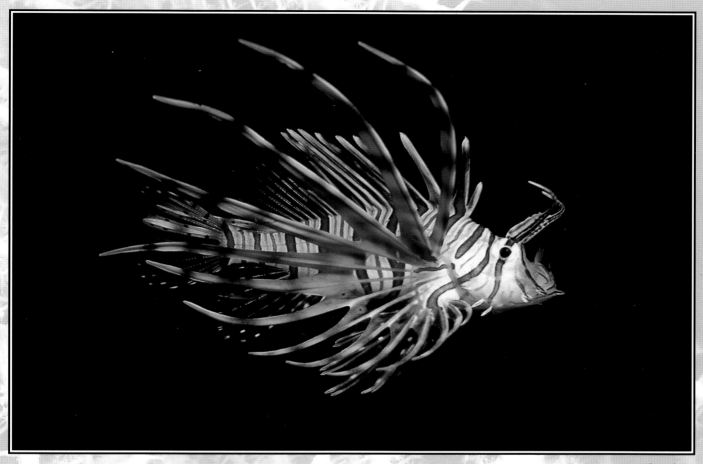

Jürgen Kuchinke

Scorpionfish (**SCORPAENIDAE**), to which family the red firefish belongs, live in all temperate seas.
They are protected by poisonous spines and should be left in peace when seen on a reef.
To alleviate the pain in case of injury the wound can be placed in very hot water and a physician should be consulted.

RED FIREFISH adult   *Pterois volitans*   Linnaeus 1758

Hans Sjöholm

Hagen Schmid

Poisonous spines are characteristic of the scorpionfish family. The most beautiful repre-
sentatives of this family are the red firefish which spread their long fins to form a "net" with
which they chase potential victims, small fish, away from the protective corals into the open
water, where they are more easily caught.
At sundown, when they often feed, groups sometimes co-ordinate their hunting activities
and encircle the prey.

Hans Sjöholm

Devil scorpionfish are lazy swimmers. They often lie almost motionless, well camouflaged between rocks or broken coral, waiting for prey, such as small crabs and fish, to approach. They adapt their colouration to their surroundings and are quite difficult to recognize.

BEARDED Scorpionfish　　*Scorpaenopsis barbatus*　　Rüppell 1838

Tuula Metcalfe

Kevin Metcalfe

The stonefish looks more like a stone overgrown with algae than a fish, hence its common name.
When a smaller animal comes close enough to investigate the "stone", the mouth bursts open, extending to over one third of the body size, and sucks in the prey.
The spines of its dorsal fin are extremely venomous.

REEF STONEFISH

Tuula Metcalfe

VELVET LEAFFISH   *Ptarmus gallus*   Kossmann & Räuber 1877

Hans Sjöholm

These fish are closely related to the scorpionfish, but belong to the **APLOACTINIDAE**, the velvetfish family.
Their skin lacks normal scales and instead has tiny bristles. These give the skin a some-what rough, velvet-like texture, and therefore the name velvet leaffish.

LEAF SCORPIONFISH   *Cocotropus steinitzi*   Eschmeyer & Dor 1978

Hans Sjöholm

Their extremely laterally, compressed bodies and high dorsal fins give these bizarrely shaped fish a leaf-like appearance.
They are often seen resting on the seafloor, rocking from side to side with the swell.

INDIAN WALKMAN   *Inimicus filamentosus*   Cuvier 1829

Hagen Schmid

Brightly coloured fins are a warning not to touch the very poisonous spines of this scorpion-fish. It hides, preferably in the sandy seafloor where only the telescopic eyes and mouth stick out and watch for prey.

Tube worm colony

Tuula Metcalfe

PIXY HAWKFISH   *Cirrhitichthys oxycephalus*   Bleeker 1855

Jürgen Kuchinke

Prominent coral outcrops on the reefs are a favourite observation post for the hawkfish to watch out for prey animals such as the crabs and small fish on which they feed.
Tiny hairs, in latin named cirrhis, on the spines of the dorsal fin, are responsible for their family name **CIRRHITIDAE.**

LONGNOSE HAWKFISH   *Oxycirrhites typus*   Bleeker 1857

Hans Sjöholm

Some fish prefer to live in association with particular coralline species. The longnose hawk-fish, for example, is mostly found in association with black coral which is found in relatively deep water and under shaded overhangs at shallower depths.

BLACKSIDE HAWKFISH   *Paracirrhites forsteri*   Schneider 1801

Simon Hackett

Hawkfish, like many reef fishes, usually live in mixed sex groups dominated by a single male. Members of the harem are similarly coloured and it is thus difficult to distinguish between the sexes. The dominant male, more easily recognisable by its behaviour, usually controls two to six females.

Lacking a swim bladder, hawkfish are relatively poor swimmers; they seem to spend most of their time resting on coral heads.

BLACKSIDE HAWKFISH

Hans Sjöholm

57

SCALEFIN ANTHIAS   *Pseudanthias squamipinnis*   Peters 1855

Kevin Metcalfe

One of the most commonly seen fish on the reefs of the central and northern Red Sea is the anthias. They live in harems in which a dominant, distinctly coloured male guards a group of females. The highest ranking female will change sex and colour to lead a harem when the dominant male dies.

MIDAS BLENNY   *Ecsenius midas*   Starck 1969

Tuula Metcalfe

Blending perfectly into a school of anthias, only an attentive observer can recognize the midas blenny. This fish adopts the colour and movements of the anthias to feed on plankton, which flows by in the water.
The name midas originates from Greek mythology: King Midas of Phrygia could convert anything into gold by touching it.

SCALEFIN ANTHIAS female

Tuula Metcalfe

SCALEFIN ANTHIAS male

Simon Hackett

CORAL GROUPER   *Cephalopholis miniata*   Forskål 1775

Hagen Schmid

Once a very common sight on Arabian coral reefs, these fish are now becoming scarce. The principal reason for this decline is spearfishing. Many animals are killed before they reach maturity and are able to reproduce.
The grouper family, **EPINEPHELINAE**, is a very important group of predatory fish. They keep a biological balance on coral reefs by culling fish populations of weak, genetically unfit individuals.

RED SEA GROUPER   *Cephalopholis hemistiktos*   Rüppell 1830

Kevin Metcalfe

This endemic fish can grow to a length of about 30 cm. They are only found in the Red Sea and along the Arabian coastline.
The fish in the picture is being cleansed of parasites by a cleaner wrasse.

Unlike their large relatives dwarf groupers are only a few centimetres long and are often brilliantly coloured.
The female deposits a mass of eggs on a rock and the male guards and cares for them.
It is believed that sex reversal is a common phenomenon with the **PSEUDOCHROMIDAE**, the family to which the dottyback belongs.

ORCHID DOTTYBACK   *Pseudochromis fridmani*   Klausewitz 1968

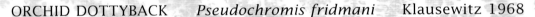

Tuula Metcalfe

Soft coral   *Dendronephthya hemprichi*

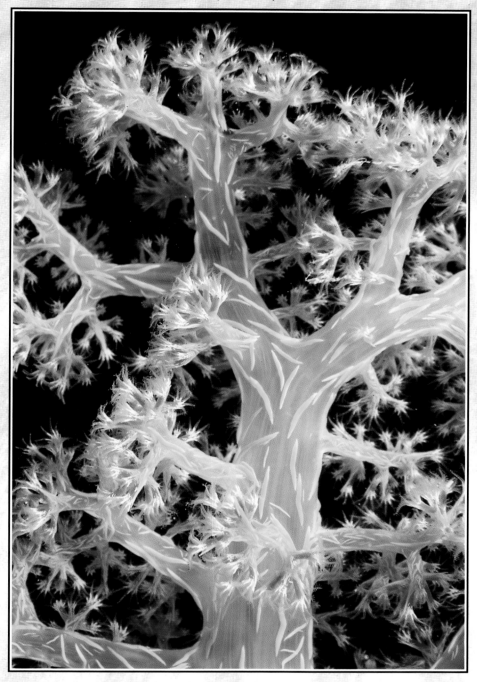

Walter Lüdin

Kevin Metcalfe

Shrimp-gobies live in burrows, which are dug and inhabited by shrimps. These shrimps are often blind or have inadequate eyesight and they gain a positive advantage by having the goby keep guard at the burrow entrance while the shrimp excavates and cleans out their shared home. For its own part, the goby gains both a place to live and a source of food among the diggings undertaken by its house-mate. Shrimps and fish maintain body contact, often through the shrimp's long feelers, and when the fish signals any danger both will dash back into their safe haven underground.

These fishes which belong to the **GOBIIDAE** family are very adaptable and inhabit many different environments.

HARLEQUIN PRAWN GOBY

Tuula Metcalfe

WHITECAP GOBY   *Lotilia graciliosa*   Klausewitz 1960
with the prawn *Alpheus rubromaculatus*

Tuula Metcalfe

The whitecap goby lives only with one particular shrimp (*Alpheus rubromaculatus*). The fish usually hovers over the burrow entrance, while the shrimp digs out the hole.

TAILSPOT GOBY   *Amblygobius albimaculatus*   Rüppell 1830

Tuula Metcalfe

CITRON GOBY   *Gobiodon citrinus*   Rüppell 1838

Jürgen Kuchinke

The citron goby lives in branching corals of the **ACROPORA** family. They are well-protected by the coral branches. Additionally they produce a toxic mucus which discourages many potential predators from attacking them.

GOBY juvenile   *Gobiodon* sp.

Charles Zoch

71

Hans Sjöholm

On whip corals one may notice small semi-transparent little fish, the whip gobies. They live mostly in pairs, male and female, on a single coral and feed on plankton flowing by. They deposit their eggs on a site which has previously been cleared of coral polyps.

WHIP GOBY   *Bryaninops yongei*   Davis & Cohen 1969

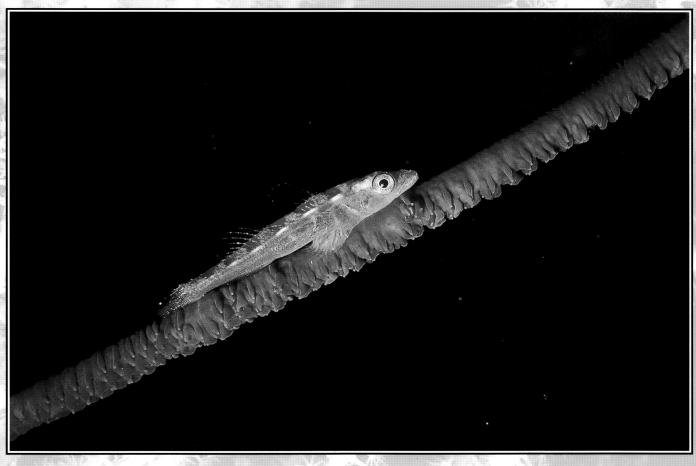

Hagen Schmid

RED EYE GOBY   *Bryaninops natans*   Larson 1985

Hans Sjöholm

CORAL GOBY   *Pleurosicya* sp.

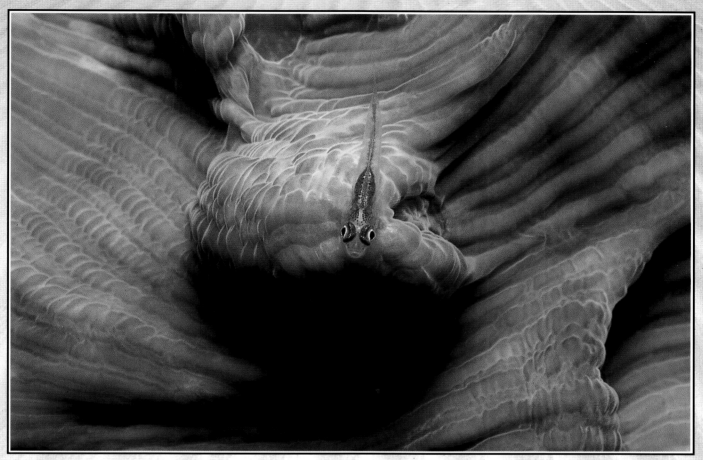

Charles Zoch

SHORT-BODIED BLENNY female   *Exallias brevis*   Kner 1868

Tuula Metcalfe

Protecting offspring is not easy on a coral reef, where lots of other hungry animals live. One animal that uses the stinging fire-coral to hide its eggs, is the short-bodied blenny of the family **BLENIIDAE**. Both parents guard the eggs until the young fish hatch.

SHORT-BODIED BLENNY male

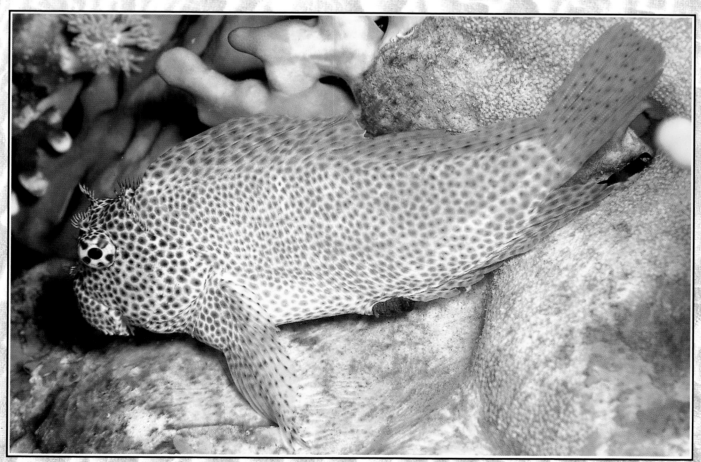

Tuula Metcalf

Wrasses are abundant inhabitants of most coral reefs. The family of **LABRIDAE** to which they belong, contains a large number of species, only exceeded by the goby family (**GOBIIDAE**).

The smallest wrasse is only a few centimetres long, whilst the largest, the hump-head, can grow to over 2 metres in length.

Most of them are brightly coloured. The colouration of juveniles and adults is often different and tends to confuse divers who try to identify these forms underwater.

Within the **LABRIDAE** family the ability to change sex is quite common with female fish later transforming into males. During the transition phase the colouration will gradually change, because males and females often show different markings. This further adds to the confusion regarding identification of some species.

Wrasses are active during the daytime; at sunset they hide between corals or dig into the sandy seafloor, where they rest during the night.

Some juveniles behave like cleaner fish and relieve other animals of parasites. This is particularly true of juvenile lyretail hogfish which are quite active cleaners.

HUMPHEAD WRASSE   *Cheilinus undulatus*   Rüppell 1835

Hagen Schmid

ROCKMOVER WRASSE   *Novaculichtys taeniourus*   Lacépède 1801

Tuula Metcalfe

Its habit of moving rocks around to find food, such as small crabs and worms which are hiding underneath, gives this little wrasse the perfect name "rockmover".

ROCKMOVER WRASSE juvenile

Kevin Metcalfe

VERMICULATE WRASSE   *Macropharyngodon bipartitus*   Smith 1957

Kevin Metcalfe

LYRETAIL HOGFISH   *Bodianus anthioides*   Bennett 1830

Tuula Metcalfe

Juvenile lyretail hogfish can sometimes be observed at "fish cleaning stations" where they clean other fish of dead skin tissue and small parasites.

EIGHT STRIPED WRASSE   *Paracheilinus octotaenia*   Fourmanior 1955

Tuula Metcalfe

Eight striped wrasses are endemic to the Red Sea and the Gulf of Aden.
The name is well chosen because of the eight stripes which the fish displays.
The male keeps a large harem and during courtship intensifies his colour.

YELLOWBREASTED WRASSE juvenile   *Anampses twistii*   Bleeker 1856

Tuula Metcalfe

An effective display of the "false eye" deception is shown by this juvenile yellowbreasted wrasse. When unfolding its dorsal and anal fins, the fish displays a pair of false eyes which confuse and scare away potential predators.

DIANAS WRASSE   *Bodianus diana*   Lacépède 1801
with CLEANER WRASSE   *Labroides dimidiatus*   Valenciennes 1839

Charles Zoch

CHECKERBOARD WRASSE   *Halichoeres hortulanus*   Lacépède 1801

Simon Hackett

Coral polyps

Hagen Schmid

Fish are very often pestered by small bloodsucking tormentors, like sealice and copepods. These crustaceans often attach themselves between the fish's gills or teeth or occasionally near its tail. The parasites weaken the host fish and, over a long period, can cause the death of the larger victim.

A group of small wrasses and shrimps have specialised in cleaning fish to get rid of these tormentors.

Fish visit cleaners regularly and special behavioural signs, generally in the form of swimming posture, signal their readiness to be cleaned. The most common signal is that the fish to be cleaned remains almost stationary, hovering in one location at the "cleaning station", opening its mouth and gill cavities widely and permitting the cleaners to remove any troublesome parasites.

SULPHUR DAMSELFISH   *Pomacentrus sulfureus*   with copepod parasite

Tuula Metcalfe

CLEANER WRASSE   *Labroides dimidiatus*   Valenciennes 1839

Simon Hackett

GIANT MORAY   *Gymnothorax javanicus*   Bleeker 1859
with BREASTSPOT CLEANER WRASSE   *Labroides pectoralis*   Randall & Springer 1975

Hans Sjöholm

Parrotfish are closely related to the wrasse family, with whom they have much in common. Scientifically they are classified under the family **SCARIDAE**.

The main difference between parrotfish and wrassses is that parrotfish have fused teeth which are effective when they feed on algae and hard coral. To scrape algae from rock surfaces or to mill down pieces of live coral, they need strong dental plates. Their beak-like teeth combined with their gaudy colours gave them their common name.

They can change sex; females turning into males. Males maintain harems of five to ten females

By milling down live hard corals, to extract the coral polyps and their symbiotic algae, parrotfish produce large quantities of sediment and are thus very important reef builders.

RUSTY PARROTFISH male   *Scarus ferrugineus*   Forskål 1775

Hagen Schmid

Tuula Metcalfe

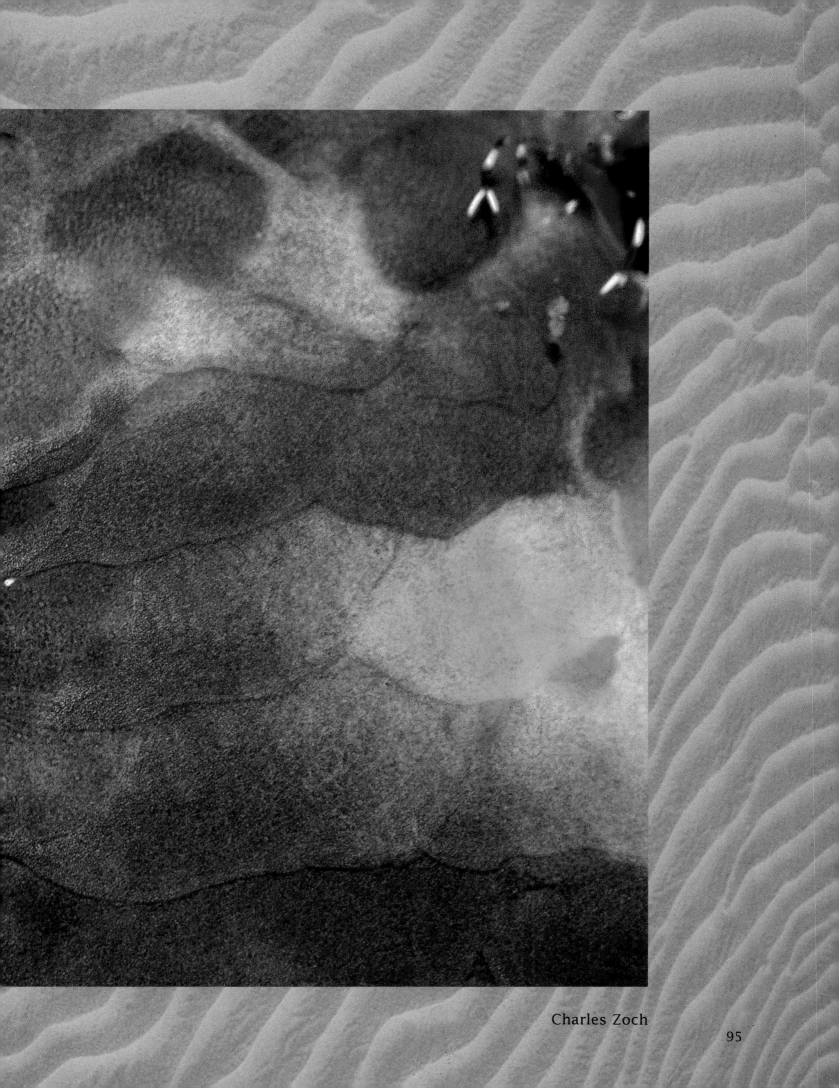

Charles Zoch

Angelfish live in all tropical seas and are often mistakenly identified as butterflyfish. Although they are related to the latter, they are classified in a different family, the **POMACANTHIDAE** which are characterised by a long spine on the lower edge of their gill plates.
The markings of juvenile angelfish are different from those of adults and they display striking colour patterns.
When disturbed some adult fish produce a loud clicking noise, which can be heard over long distances underwater.

YELLOWBAR ANGELFISH   *Pomacanthus maculosus*   Forskål 1775

Jürgen Kuchinke

BICOLOUR PARROTFISH early juvenile stage   *Cetoscarus bicolor*   Rüppell 1829

Tuula Metcalfe

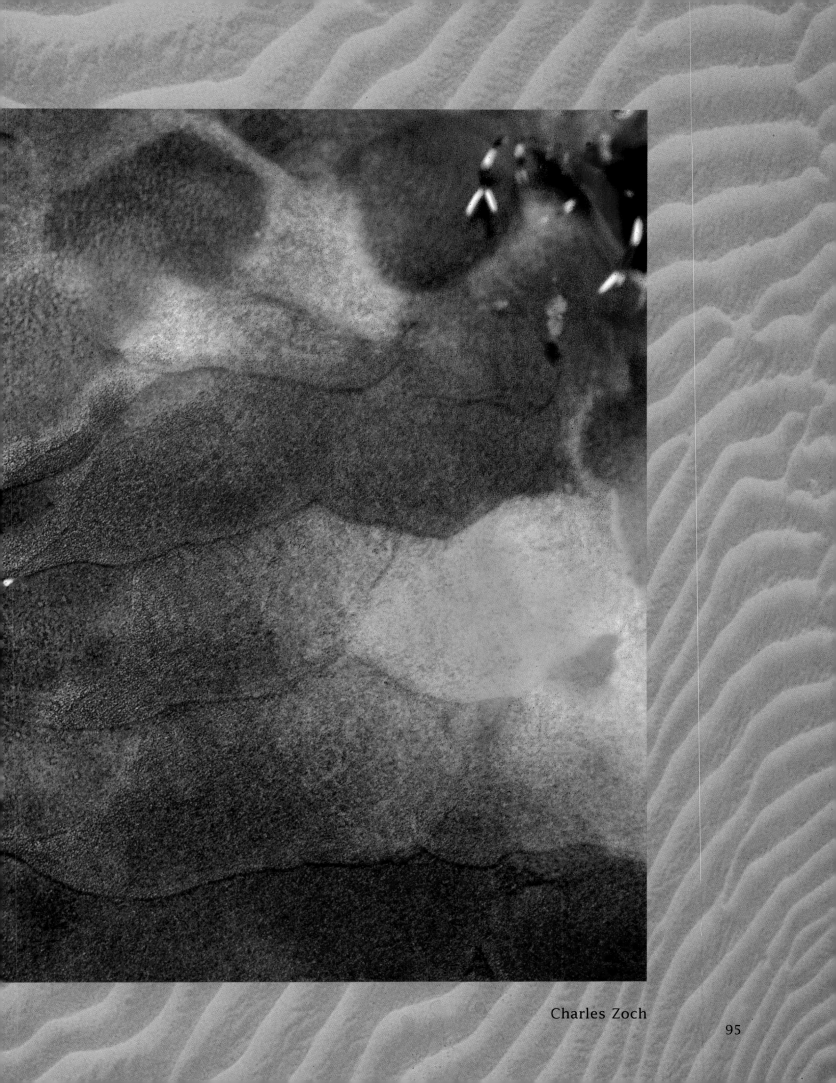

Charles Zoch

Angelfish live in all tropical seas and are often mistakenly identified as butterflyfish. Although they are related to the latter, they are classified in a different family, the **POMACANTHIDAE** which are characterised by a long spine on the lower edge of their gill plates.
The markings of juvenile angelfish are different from those of adults and they display striking colour patterns.
When disturbed some adult fish produce a loud clicking noise, which can be heard over long distances underwater.

YELLOWBAR ANGELFISH   *Pomacanthus maculosus*   Forskål 1775

Jürgen Kuchinke

96

YELLOWBAR ANGELFISH juvenile stage

Simon Hackett

Juvenile fish have a very low survival rate and the animal in our photograph has already had part of its tail nipped off by a hungry predator.

Displaying striking colours as one would expect of a real emperor, this reef dweller, the emperor angelfish, is one of the most beautiful fish we may encounter in tropical waters.

EMPEROR ANGELFISH   *Pomacanthus imperator*   Bloch 1787

Simon Hackett

Jürgen Kuchinke

ROYAL ANGELFISH   *Pygoplites diacanthus*   Boddaert 1772

Jürgen Kuchinke

Young fish sometimes display "false eye"; colour markings near the tail. This confuses potential predators, and gives the animal a better chance of survival.

ROYAL ANGELFISH juvenile

Kevin Metcalfe

ZEBRA ANGELFISH male   *Genicanthus caudovittatus*   Günther 1860

Tuula Metcalfe

Zebra angelfish live at certain steep drop offs on coral reefs, at a depth of 20 to 30 metres. They are very timid and difficult to approach.

ZEBRA ANGELFISH female

Tuula Metcalfe

Butterflyfish were so named because they are graceful swimmers and exhibit extraordinary colour patterns.
They belong to the **CHAETODONTIDAE** family.
In the Red Sea 14 species are found of which seven are native to the Red Sea and the Gulf of Aden. They feed mainly on coral polyps., but some feed on algae and invertebrates.

CHEVRON BUTTERFLYFISH   *Chaetodon trifascialis*   Quoy & Gaimard 1824

Simon Hackett

Simon Hackett

Simon Hackett

CROWN BUTTERFLYFISH   *Chaetodon paucifasciatus*   Ahl 1923

Simon Hackett

STRIPED BUTTERFLYFISH   *Chaetodon fasciatus*   Forskål 1775

Walter Lüdin

Hagen Schmid

Hagen Schmid

Tuula Metcalfe

Sweetlips or grunts, as they are also known, can be found in all tropical seas.
There are about 120 species in the family of **HAEMULIDAE** to which they belong.
Usually called sweetlips in reference to their small thick-lipped mouths, their alternative common name, grunts, derives from a grunting noise that they make when grinding their pharyngeal teeth. The sound is amplified by a gas bladder.
Young fish go through colour changes while maturing.

BLACK-BLOTCHED PORCUPINEFISH   *Diodon liturosus*   Shaw 1804

Hans Sjöholm

Slow swimming fish need effective protection against predators.
Porcupinefish of the **DIODONTIDAE** family can double their body size by drawing water into the abdomen. Additionally they are armed with long sharp spines. When in danger, these animals expand their bodies and the spines project perpendicularly, protecting the fish.
Once very common on shallow reefs, these fish are disappearing rapidly, primarily because their defensive responses of inflating their size and priming their spiny armour render them almost immobile and, thus, all too easy a target for inexperienced spearfishermen and for commercial collectors.

PORCUPINEFISH   *Diodon hystrix*   Linnaeus 1758

Hans Sjöholm

STAR PUFFERFISH juvenile   *Arothron stellatus*   Bloch & Schneider 1801

Charles Zoch

Box- or trunkfishes of the **OSTRACIIDAE** family possess a unique shaped carapace. It can be quadrangular, triangular or round.
The animals are slow swimmers and are protected by their very rigid skeleton. Additionally some of them can release, in stress situations, a poisonous mucus called ostracitoxin.
The young of the yellow boxfish are coloured with black spots, which have the same size and shape as their eyes, to confuse potential predators.

YELLOW BOXFISH juvenile   *Ostracion cubicus*   Linnaeus 1758

Hans Sjöholm

115

VIPER FLOUNDR   *Soleichthys heterorhinos*   Bleeker 1856

Hans Sjöholm

Its snake-like swimming movements give the viper flounder its name. It is active during the night; in the daytime it rests buried under sand.
Scientifically it is a member of the **SOLEIDAE** family.

VIPER FLOUNDER

Hans Sjöholm

Tuula Metcalfe

Sea moth fish, of the **PEGASIDAE** family, live on sandy seafloors or in sea-grass. These fish can hardly swim and "walk" on the sea-floor with the help of their fins.

SPECKLED SANDPERCH   *Parapercis hexophtalma*   Cuvier 1829

Tuula Metcalfe

Members of the **BALISTIDAE** family possess a trigger-like first dorsal spine which can be locked in position by a smaller second spine. This characteristic gives the trigger fish its common name. At night they sleep in holes and secure themselves with their locked trigger-like spine.
They possess strong teeth with which they crack open shells and crabs.
Some build a nest by excavating a crater-like cavity, in which they deposit their eggs. These are guarded by the fish and any intruder, even a diver, is aggressively chased away.

ORANGE-LINED TRIGGERFISH   *Balistapus undulatus*   Park 1797

Hagen Schmid

TITAN TRIGGERFISH   *Balistoides viridescens*   Bloch & Schneider 1801

Hans Sjöholm

HARLEQUIN GHOSTPIPEFISH   *Solenostomus paradoxus*   Pallas 1870

Hans Sjöholm

Their very unusual shape and their ability to adapt to the colour of their surroundings, make the ghostpipefish masters of camouflage.
Scientifically they are classified in the **SOLENOSTOMIDAE** family and are related to the pipefish.
The female fish incubates her eggs in a small pouch formed by the enlarged pelvic fin.

Close up of HARLEQUIN GHOSTPIPEFISH

Hans Sjöholm

NETWORK PIPEFISH   *Corythoichthys flavofasciatus*   Rüppell 1838

Simon Hackett

The long slender body consists of ring-like bony segments and gives these animals their name of pipefish. They belong to the **SYNGNATHIDAE** family, together with the more commonly known seahorse.
An unusual characteristic of these fish is that the male carries the fertilized eggs in a pouch until the young animals hatch.

MANY-BANDED PIPEFISH   *Doryrhamphus multiannulatus*   Regan 1903

Kevin Metcalfe

BLUESTRIPE PIPEFISH   *Doryrhamphus excisus abbreviatus*

Jürgen Kuchinke

The colourful pipefish of the Doryrhamphus group has a preference to hide between the protecting spines of sea-urchins.

Mouth of MUSHROOM CORAL   *Fungia* sp.

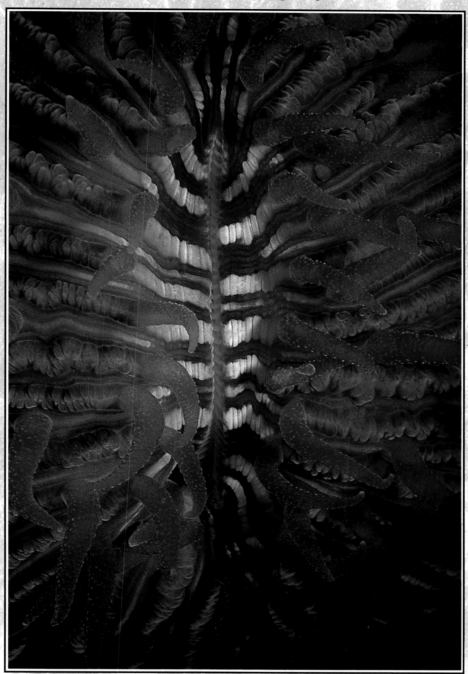

Hagen Schmid

From shark fossil records we know that the ancestors of sharks existed 450 million years ago. Although these ancient sharks are extinct, there are eight surviving species (the **HETERODONTIDAE** family), which can be traced back approximately 180 million years.

More "modern" sharks, like the family **CARCHARHINIDAE**, go back less than 100 million years. This family consists of 48 species and includes open water sharks and tropical reef dwellers. Their body form has adapted to their way of life. The open water ones have a streamlined slender shape and are fast swimmers. The bottom dwellers are mostly more bulky and do not travel more than is necessary to find food.

About 350 types of sharks roam the oceans, from the 24 cm long cat shark (*Eridacnis radcliffei*) to the large whale shark (*Rhinocodon typus*) that can grow to 15 metres and is the largest fish in the sea.

Some sharks live in the cold waters of the polar regions, others prefer the warmer temperatures of the tropical seas.

Their diet consist of crustaceans, sea urchins, fish, marine mammals or plankton, depending on the species and environment they live in.

In the Red Sea we find 35 to 40 different types of sharks, from the aggressive ocean whitetip (*Carcharhinus longimanus*) to the rather docile leopard shark (*Stegostoma fasciatum*).

Sharks do not posses a gas bladder as bony fish do. They keep buoyant thanks to their relatively large oily liver, which can be over 20% of their body weight. Their bony structure exists of a cartilaginous skeleton, which is more elastic and lighter than bones. Owing to this, they need to spend less energy on buoyancy control.

The skin of sharks is not smooth, but more like sand paper and appears to increase drag when swimming. Actually it provides a laminar flow and reduces friction. It also makes sharks hydrodynamic which enables them to move fast and very quietly in the water. Some open water sharks can reach speeds of over 60 km per hour in short sprints

The reproduction rate of sharks is very low. They also grow very slowly and reach sexual maturity only after several years.

Sharks are not vicious uncontrolled killers, as often characterized. However, these fish should be treated with respect, when an encounter takes place. The danger from them is greatly exaggerated and adds to a rather negative image of these ancient survivors.

Overfishing in all oceans has hit the shark population very hard and in some seas these magnificent animals are becoming close to extinction because of human interference. Everything possible should be done to regulate fishing activities world wide to save these sharks.

SILKY SHARK   *Carcharhinus falciformis*   Bibron 1839
with pilotfish *Naucrates ductor* in front of him

Gerry Pyke

SILKY SHARK feeding on cuttlefish

Gerry Pyke

WHALE SHARK   *Rhincodon typus*   Smith 1828

Tuula Metcalfe

PLANKTONIC NUDIBRANCH   *Glaucilla marginata*   Bergh

Jürgen Kuchinke

132

Nudibranchs are sea snails without external shells and are common in all oceans; however, most of the approximately 3000 known species live in tropical seas, and are variable in form, size, and colour. The smallest are only a few millimetres long, the largest ones can reach a length of 20–30 centimetres.

Some nudibranchs feed on sponges, others on bryozoans, hydroids, coral polyps or fish eggs, and some are even cannibalistic and prey on other nudibranchs.

Often exhibiting gaudy colours, these creatures move slowly over the sea floor searching for mates or prey.

Some nudibranchs are strictly nocturnal, others are more active during daytime, depending upon their feeding habits.

Nudibranchs are bisexual: both male and female at the same time. The partners fertilize each other's eggs, which are then deposited by the animals in characteristic egg masses on the sea floor, or on food substrate

In some species, young larvae hatch with a protective shell and float with the water currents. In others, the young hatch as miniature adults, without a planktonic feeding stage.

The life span of nudibranchs varies from a few weeks to more than one year.

For an underwater photographer nudibranchs are always a fascinating subject. They usually display bright colours and because they can not move away rapidly it is easy to focus a camera lens on them.

A sub-order of the order *Nudibranchia* is the *Aeolidacea*. These animals can be recognized by their very slender body and the colourful projections on their back. These projections are armed with stinging cells and discourage potential predators. The slugs do not produce these cells, but collect them with their food and then place them in the projections, called corata, which actually contain extended digestive glands. When a predator tries to eat one of these aeolids, it gets badly stung by the exploding cells.

NUDIBRANCH   *Gymnodoris* sp.   laying eggs

Charles Zoch

NUDIBRANCH   *Nembrotha megalocera*   feeding on *Tunicate*

Hans Sjöholm

AEOLID NUDIBRANCH   *Eubranchus* sp.

Charles Zoch

AEOLID NUDIBRANCH   *Flabellina* sp.   feeding on red sponge

Kevin Metcalfe

AEOLID NUDIBRANCH   *Spurilla* sp.

Jürgen Kuchinke

OPISTHOBRANCH   *Caliphylla* sp.

Jürgen Kuchinke

Opisthobranchea are not part of the nudibranch family. These animals belong to the **SACOGLOSSEA** family and are herbivorous. They prefer to feed on sap of algae or other plants which grow in shallow water.

No group of shells arouses our enthusiasm and interest more than cowrie shells. Some Pacific islanders believe that these shells posses magic powers and can influence the fisherman's catch or a woman's fertility.

The beautiful, glossy surfaces, intricately patterned and strikingly coloured shells are frequently used as ornaments or amulets.

Cowries are tropical sea shells and feed on algae or invertebrates.

PANTHER COWRIE SHELL   *Cypraea pantherina*   Lightfoot 1786

Hans Sjöholm

TRITON SHELL   *Charonia tritonis*   Linnaeus 1758

Hans Sjöholm

Members of the Triton family include some of the largest living gastropods.
Due to their nocturnal habits, these shells are rarely seen on coral reefs during the day.
Unfortunately their attractive colouration and their large size make these animals popular
collectors' items.

Squid and cuttlefish possess ink-sacs and skin with pigment cells. When they are in danger, they release an ink-cloud to confuse predators. Additionally, they change their colouration to blend in with their surroundings. This gives the animals a good chance of escaping their numerous enemies.
They are closely related to the cowrie shells, although in appearance they are more like the octopus.

CUTTLEFISH   *Sephia pharaonis*

Hans Sjöholm

BOTTLE TAILED SQUID   *Sepioteuthis lessoniana*

Hans Sjöholm

In the Red Sea we can find about 15 different species of jellyfish. The most common ones belong to the Aurelia family, which do not posses long stinging tentacles and are harmless.

During spring time they can suddenly occur in large numbers and then mysteriously disappear again after a few weeks. The explanation for these sudden appearances is to be found in their life cycle.

Jellyfish fertilize their eggs internally, following which a small ciliated larva develops, which eventually emerges from the adult jellyfish's mouth and then floats with the water currents. Drifting within the plankton, the larva gradually changes shape, developing polyp-like tentacles, and sinks to the seafloor where it settles and forms a reproductive polyp called scyphistoma. Out of this, on top of each other (like a stack of plates) jellyfish larvae called ephyra develop. After a few months they split off and drift with the water current, eventually growing into full size jellyfish.

These animals possess one of the most simple nervous systems and propel themselves by rhythmically contracting their bell-shaped bodies. They do not drift in the sea without any sense of direction, but purposefully move over long distances, making regular journeys to the seafloor or to the surface, depending on the supply of plankton, which is their main food.

Many of the jellyfish have stinging tentacles with which they paralyze their prey before manoeuvring it into their mouth.

Some animals are immune to the poisonous tentacles and hide inside them. They travel with their host, well protected against any predators.

Hagen Schmid

Fish hiding inside jellyfish

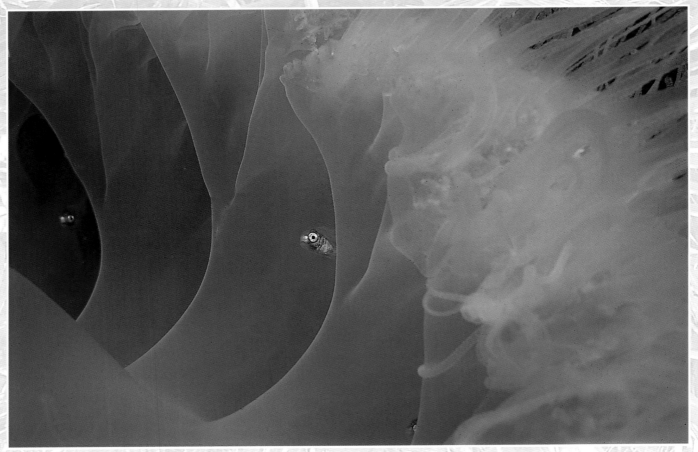

Hans Sjöholm

Jellyfish with brittle star

Hagen Schmid

SEASPIDER   *Hyastenus* sp.   in *Dendronephthya* soft coral

Jürgen Kuchinke

Crustaceans live on beaches, in shallow water and at great depths, and inhabit every environment. Millions float in the arctic seas and are the main food source for the largest animals, the whales. Other relatives live on tropical reefs and clean fish of parasites. With more than 10,000 known species, shrimps and crabs are the most diverse group of marine animals. A small anemone shrimp will grow to a few millimetres in length while the large japanese spider crab can reach 3 metres in size with stretched legs.

Shrimps and crabs feed on plankton, algae, invertebrates and dead animals. With their superb sense of smell they can locate decomposing material over long distances and then consume it. By doing this, the animals play an important ecological role in the sea.

They have open blood circulation; their blood does not flow in vessels, but in spaces between the organs. To prevent losing too much blood during an attack, the animals are well prepared. When in danger, they can discard a leg by contracting a muscle and close the resulting small opening with a skin partition. With the next moult, which shrimps and crabs undergo regularly, the lost leg will grow back again.

Most interesting, is their ability to protect themselves from their numerous predators. They can live together with stinging sea anemones, or take on the colour of animals like the spanish dancer (nudibranch) and then hide themselves in the gills of this animal. They move into an empty shell and retreat when necessary, or allow additional anemones to attach and grow on their outer shell as a further protection. They live in soft corals or sponges and adopt the colour of their host, or even transfer sponges and corals onto their body, where they will grow. They may even wear small anemones on their pincers to scare off predators.

Shrimps and crabs are masters of camouflage and adapt themselves perfectly in their environment.

FEATHER STAR *Lamprometra klunzingeri*

Tuula Metcalfe

At night feather stars (Crinoids) leave their hiding places and crawl to the upper branches of the coral refuge, to which they attach themselves tightly, while spreading their arms to form a plankton-collecting sieve in the water current.
Many crinoids are host to other creatures, like shrimps and crabs. These adapt to the colours of their host and hide, well camouflaged, between its arms.

CRINOID CRAB   *Ceratocarcinus* cf. spinosus   in feather star

Tuula Metcalfe

DECORATOR CRAB   *Ophthalmias* sp.   with sponge as camouflage

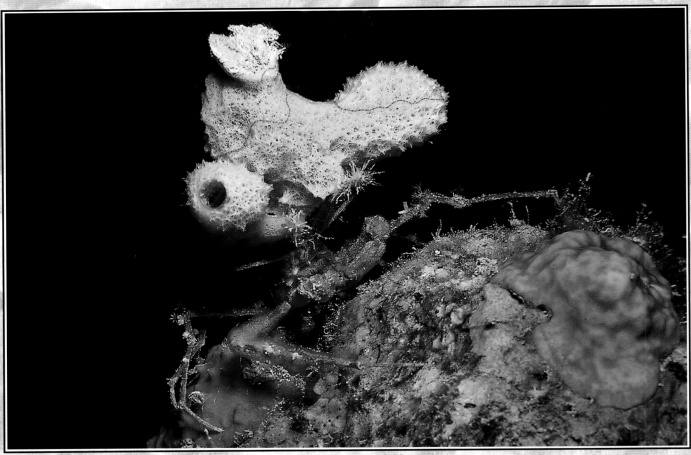

Hans Sjöholm

From time to time, when growing up, crustaceans shed their hard outer shell.
Decorator crabs are able to transplant their decoration to the new shell with the help of their
pincers. They use a glue-like liquid produced by a special gland to attach the camouflage to
their shells.

DECORATOR CRAB   *Chlorinoides* sp.   with xenia polyps camouflage

Jürgen Kuchinke

HERMIT CRAB   *Dardanus pedunculatus*   with calliactis anemone on shell

Tuula Metcalfe

Hermit crabs protect their soft body and tail in a suitable housing, like an empty shell.
When growing up, the shell is replaced regularly by a larger one.
Some hermit crabs of the Dardanus family plant stinging polyps on their housing to scare
off predators.

PAINTED CRAYFISH juvenile   *Panulirus versicolor*

Hans Sjöholm

SPANISH DANCER NUDIBRANCH PARTNERSHRIMP   *Periclimenes imperator*

Hans Sjöholm

These shrimps prefer to live in the gills of the spanish dancer nudibranch, and adopt the red hue of their host.

Gills of SPANISH DANCER NUDIBRANCH   *Hexabranchus sanguineus*

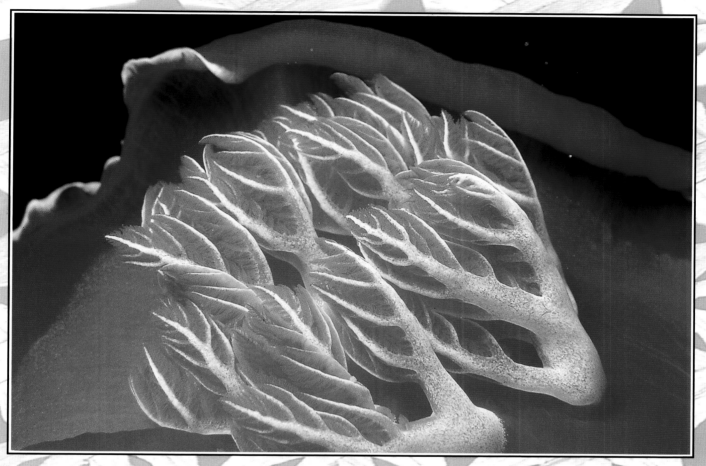

Hans Sjöholm

PARTNERSHRIMP   *Periclimenes imperator*

Charles Zoch

Sea cucumbers (*Holothuroidea*) and sea urchins (*Echinoidea*) are a favourite host for tiny shrimps. By adopting the colours of their surroundings, they are nearly invisible and therefore safe from predators.

HUMP-BACKED SHRIMP   *Saron marmoratus*

Tuula Metcalfe

Shrimps are, like many crustaceans, night-active animals. Most of them do not move far away from the protecting coral reef. They prefer to wander around the reeftop where the water current brings them an ample food supply.

Jürgen Kuchinke

RED SEA HUMP-BACKED SHRIMP   *Rhynchocinetidae* sp.

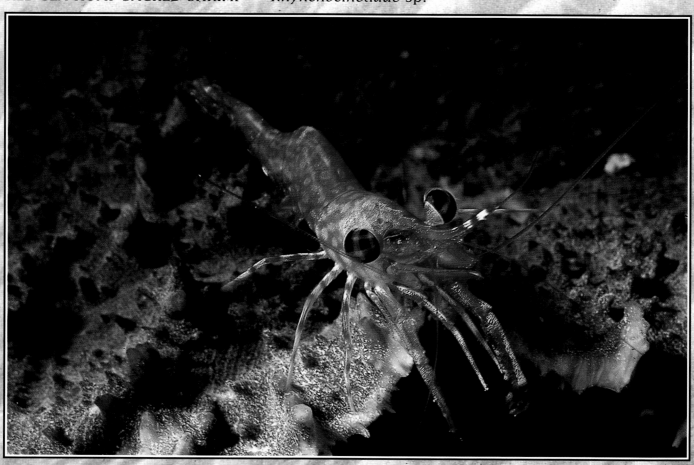

Hagen Schmid

GLOSSY IBIS   *Plegadis falcinellus*   Linnaeus 1766

Peter Dixon

The glossy ibis finds its food, mainly small fish, snails and crustaceans, in shallow water. These birds are winter guests in Saudi Arabia and profit from the many irrigation projects in this country.

BALD IBIS.   *Geronticus eremita*   Linnaeus 1758

P. & J. Gasperetti

The name of this rare bird, who is close to extinction, is bald or hermit ibis. Their last remaining retreats are in Morocco and Algeria. During migration they are rare guests in Arabia.
Until the 17th century the bald ibis nested in Central Europe, but was eradicated by over-hunting and the collecting of its nestlings.

Abyssinian rollers got the name "roller" because of the acrobatic flight the male bird makes as it displays to attract a female during the mating season.
They feed on insects, mice and small reptiles.

ABYSSINIAN ROLLER   *Coracias abyssinica*   Hermann 1783

P. & J. Gasperetti

These very colourful birds feed not only on bees, but also on larger insects, like dragonflies and butterflies. They are swift and graceful flyers and catch their prey in the air.

RED-TAILED CHAT   *Cercomela familiaris*   Cabanis 1875

Peter Dixon

SPOTTED FLYCATCHER   *Muscicapa striata*   Pallas 1764

Simon Priscott

ISABELLINE SHRIKE   *Lanius isabellinus*   Hemprich & Ehrenberg 1833

Peter Dixon

Shrikes hunt insects and small lizards. Sometimes they impale their catch on sharp thorns to devour at a later date.

Peter Dixon

No other bird masters the art of building a nest as the weaver-bird does. The work is done by the male bird, who learns "the weaving" from older, more experienced birds. The female bird inspects the nest and only accepts its builder when the construction is perfectly woven.

Young eagle owls in nest

Simon Priscott

Peter Dixon

P. & J. Gasperetti

During winter migration hoopoes are common visitors on the large empty plains of Arabia.

HOOPOE   *Upupa epops*   Linnaeus 1758

P. & J. Gasperetti

P. & J. Gasperetti

Garden dormice are night-active animals, which feed on fruits and seeds.

DESERT FOX   *Vulpes vulpes arabica*   Thomas 1902

Peter Dixon

Desert foxes are smaller than most of their relatives in other parts of the world. They are well adapted to the harsh and hot desert climate conditions. The large eyes and ears are characteristic of these shy predators.

The inaccessible mountain regions of the Arabian Peninsula are the last retreats of the ibex.

IBEX   *Capra ibex nubiana*   Cuvier 1825

Peter Dixon

Young IBEX

Peter Dixon

ARABIAN ORYX   *Oryx leucorys*   Pallas 1777

Peter Dixon

Extensive breeding programs have been undertaken by the Saudi Arabian government to reintroduce the arabian oryx into the wild. These animals were once almost extinct due to overhunting and the destruction of their habitat.

HAMADRYAS BABOON   *Papio hamadryas*   Thomas 1900

Hagen Schmid

Baboons are among the few wild animals whose population has recently increased, owing to the disappearance of their natural predators, like the arabian leopard, the hyena and the wolf.

LANNER FALCON   *Falco biarmicus*   Temminck 1825

Peter Dixon

Hunting with falcons has a long tradition on the Arabian Peninsula.

Walter Lüdin

Nowadays many Bedouins keep their camels as live-stock and do not use them anymore as pack-animals to cross the desert.

The village of Dhee-Ain

Hagen Schmid

Mosque on the Red Sea shore

Hagen Schmid

Jeddah old and new

Hagen Schmid

In 1820 the German traveller Eduard Rüppell visited the town of Jeddah. He wrote the following:

". . . All of its houses are built in coral stone, several storeys high, with beautiful façades and comfortably furnished. The roads are straight, spacious and clean . . . '

Today the old Jeddah is still well preserved; many of the old buildings have been restored and blend harmoniously with the newer, more modern, constructions.

Hagen Schmid

Today modern office buildings dominate the skyline of Jeddah.

187

Hagen Schmid

Many of the old houses in Jeddah are richly decorated with wooden lattice work bow windows, to give shade and privacy.

Street in the old soukh of Jeddah

Hagen Schmid

Tuula Metcalfe

INDEX

COMMON NAME INDEX OF INVERTEBRATES   PAGE

COMMON NAME INDEX OF BIRDS   PAGE

COMMON NAME INDEX OF MAMMALS   PAGE

SCIENTIFIC INDEX OF INVERTEBRATES   PAGE

SCIENTIFIC INDEX OF BIRDS   PAGE

SCIENTIFIC INDEX OF MAMMALS   PAGE

Cover photograph by: Jürgen Kuchinke
Photographs on page 184 by: Walter Lüdin   left top and bottom
                           Hagen Schmid right top
                           Bizzie Frost   right bottom

Recommended literature for fish identification:

Fishes of the Great Barrier Reef and Coral Sea
by John E. Randall – Gerald R. Allen – Roger C. Steene
      University of Hawaii Press

Indian Ocean Tropical Fish Guide
by Helmut Debelius

Southeast Asia Tropical Fish Guide
by Helmut Debelius & Rudie H. Kuiter
      Ikan Publishing, Frankfurt

Coral Reef Fishes Indo-Pacific & Caribbean
by Ewald Lieske & Robert Myers
      Harper-Collins Publishing

Red Sea Invertebrates
by Dr. Peter Vine
      Immel Publishing

All photographers used Uwatec (Aladin Pro) diving computers.

All rights reserved. No part of this publication may be reproduced, stored in a retrieval system, or transmitted in any form or by any means, electronic, mechanical, photocopying, recording or otherwise, without the prior permission of the publisher.

Printed in Hong Kong by Paramount Printing Co. Ltd.